This book belongs to:

Amy Kate Veitch

Rainbow Unicorns Annual 2021

A Laughing Lobster Book 978-1-910765-42-5

Published in Great Britain by Laughing Lobster
an imprint of Centum Publishing Ltd.

This edition published 2020.
1 3 5 7 9 10 8 6 4 2

Illustrations by Charlotte Archer.

Laughing Lobster an imprint of Centum Publishing Ltd, 20 Devon Square,
Newton Abbot, Devon, TQ12 2HR, UK

books@centumpublishingltd.co.uk

LAUGHING LOBSTER AN IMPRINT OF CENTUM PUBLISHING
Limited Reg. No. 08497203

A CIP catalogue record for this book is available
from the British Library.

Printed in China.

Rainbow Unicorns
Annual 2021

Welcome

Come join the Rainbow Unicorns in this magical book.

Come and say hi on page 10.

Discover all about the Rainbow Unicorns and their friends on the cute profile pages in this book.

Fly to page 30 for a fun game - who will get to Unicorn Castle first? Then zoom to page 28 to create your own unicorn and page 24 to make some sparkly glitter.

Add a rainbow of colours to all the creative colouring pages inside.

Get your brain in gear with all the magical puzzles, from mazes to lots to spot!

Check out pages 49 to 54 – there are lots of creative crafts to make including a pen pot, a unicorn mask and a secret treasure box.

You can find all the answers for the puzzles at the back of the book.

Lots to spot

Can you spot...?

8 ladybirds ✓	4 clouds ✓
7 unicorns ✓	3 flags ✓
6 butterflies ✓	2 frogs ✓
5 birds ✓	1 rainbow ✓

9

Sparkle Unicorn

Meet daring
and dazzling
Sparkle Unicorn.

Sparkles make everything better!

SPECIES: unicorn
LIVES IN: Unicorn Castle
LIKES: her friends, cupcakes
              and flying

Rainbow Unicorn

Cute and colourful Rainbow Unicorn loves to look her best.

SPECIES: unicorn
LIVES IN: Unicorn Castle
LIKES: rainbows, fashion accessories and grooming her mane

How do I look?

Spot it

Can you spot 8 differences between the pictures below?

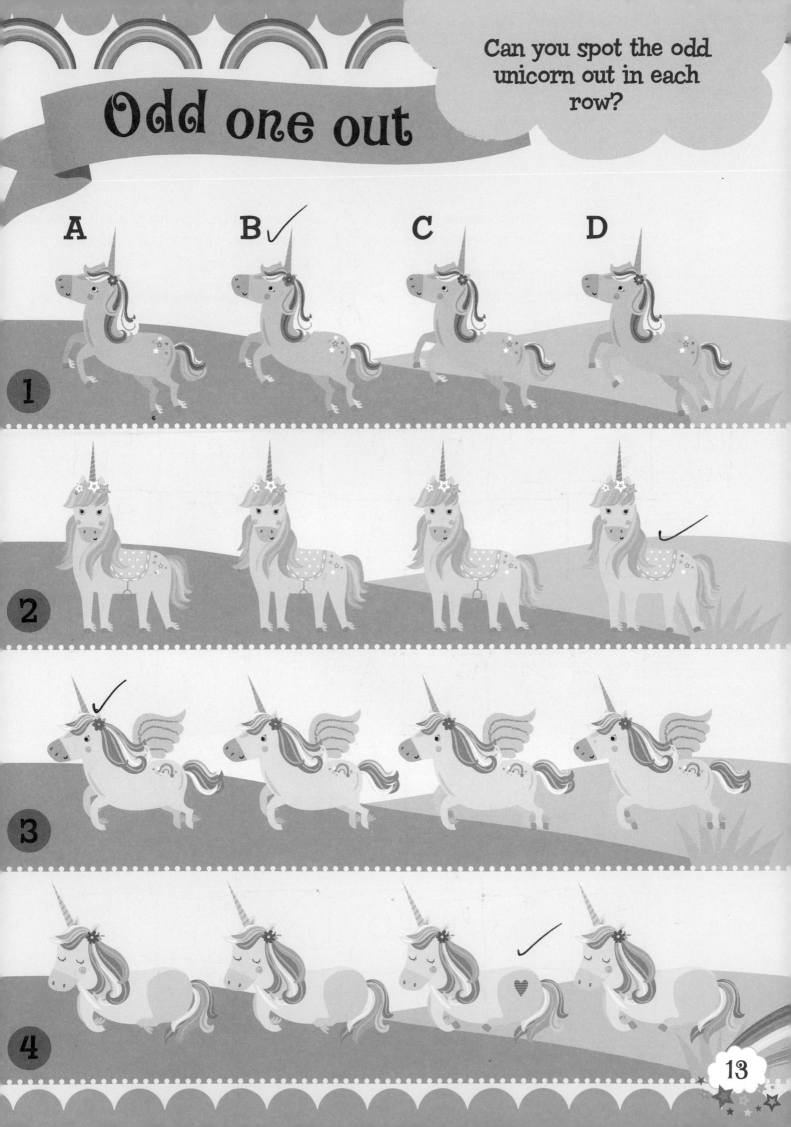

Odd one out

Can you spot the odd unicorn out in each row?

A   B ✓   C   D

1

2

3

4

Dot to dot

1. Take it in turns to draw a vertical or horizontal line between each dot.

2. Each time you complete a box, mark your initials inside it.

3. An empty box is worth 1 point, a star box is worth 2 points, a heart box is worth 3 points, a rainbow box is worth 4 points and a unicorn box is worth 5 points.

4. When all the dots have been joined up, add up your scores. The player with the most points, wins.

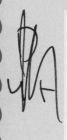

Shimmer Unicorn

Meet Shimmer Unicorn who loves parties!

Let's have a party!

SPECIES:	unicorn
LIVES IN:	Unicorn Castle
LIKES:	cupcakes, presents and balloons

Chirpy Chick

This cheeky chick is a fun friend of the Rainbow Unicorns.

Chirp chirp!

SPECIES: chick
LIVES IN: the enchanted forest
LIKES: chatting, stories and
            visiting her friends
            for tea parties
            at Unicorn Castle

Perfect patterns

Doodle a picture to complete these patterns below.

1

2

3

4

5

18

Rainbow colours

Finish off this unicorn with your brightest rainbow colours.

Fluttershy Butterfly

Let's play hide and seek!

Fluttershy is lots of fun and always up for some games.

SPECIES: butterfly
LIVES IN: the enchanted forest
LIKES: flowers, flying and playing games

Starlight Unicorn

Meet Starlight, who always wishes upon a star when she spots one in the sky.

Let's have a sleepover!

SPECIES: unicorn
LIVES IN: Unicorn Castle
LIKES: shooting stars, midnight feasts and dancing

Secret note

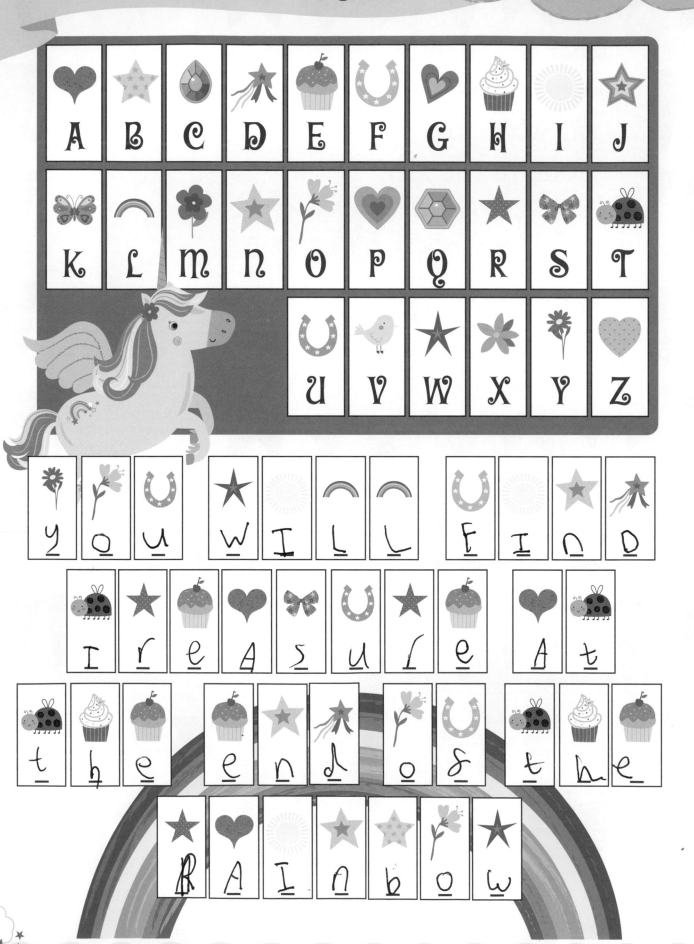

you WILL FIND
I reasure At
t he end of the
RAINbow

22

Which way?

Can you help this unicorn find her way through the maze to reach the castle?

End

Start

Glitter on!

Shimmer and sparkle with this super slime recipe!

You will need:

100ml PVA white glue (children's craft glue or CE marked glue)

½ tsp bicarbonate of soda

gel food colouring

1 tsp contact lens cleaning solution

glitter (eco)

1. Ask an adult to help and squeeze 100ml of glue into a mixing bowl. Add the bicarbonate of soda and give it a really good mix.

2. Now choose your colour. Add a drop or two of gel food colouring. Using less will make a pastel colour – adding more will make the colour brighter. Mix until totally combined.

3. Add the contact lens solution and mix again. The slime will begin to appear, going stringy then coming away clean from the bowl into a ball. Once this happens, take the ball out and knead it with your hands. It will be sticky at first but after about 30 seconds it'll turn smooth.

4. Sprinkle your eco glitter on a clean surface and roll the ball of slime in it. Now knead and mix until the glitter is mixed with the slime. Store in a pot with a lid to keep it fresh!

Dotty pals

Join the dots and transform these unicorns with your brightest colours.

Fun friends

Can you spot 10 differences between these pictures?
Colour in the hearts when you find them.

Unicorn creation

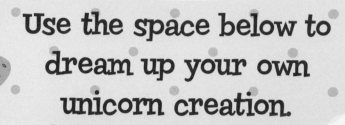

Use the space below to dream up your own unicorn creation.

If your unicorn could choose a pet, which animal would it be?

Put a tick next to the things your unicorn would like:

What would your unicorn's special skills be?

fantastic flying

baking

granting wishes

changing colours

other: _____

What colour would your unicorn's wings be?

pink

blue

yellow

purple

green

What would your
unicorn's name be?
Write it here.

ELLIE

Draw your unicorn below.

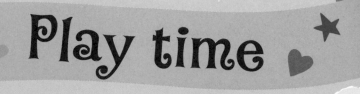

Play time

3

2
Oops, you get lost in a cloud. Miss a go.

1
Start

12
Oh no! You dropped your magical jewels. Go back to the start.

11

13
Fuel up on cake and fly on 2 clouds.

10
Slide down the rainbow to cloud 15.

14
Stop to enjoy this unicorn's birthday party and miss a go.

15

16
Stop for a snooze and miss a go.

17
Name 3 animals with a tail. Have another go.

You will need a die and two coins to play this game.

Find a friend or friends to play with.

Take it in turns to roll the die and move your coins through the clouds to help the unicorns reach the castle.

❀

Follow the instructions and complete the tasks as you go. The first one to reach the castle, wins!

4
Stop to help a bird find his nest. Miss a go.

5
Name 5 colours that appear in a rainbow. Have another go.

6
Stop for a chat with a ladybird. Miss a go.

9

8
Win a flying race with a butterfly. Zoom on 2 clouds.

7

19

20
End

18
Oh dear, you dropped your accessories. Go back to cloud 9.

Rainbow Falls

Add some shimmery colours to Rainbow Waterfall.

Filbert Frog

Ribbit ribbit!

Meet Filbert, a hoppy, happy buddy to the Rainbow Unicorns.

SPECIES: frog
LIVES IN: the enchanted pond
LIKES: jumping, swimming and poking his tongue out

Ha ha! What's a frog's favourite game? Croak-et!

33

Match up

Can you help this unicorn tidy up by matching all the accessories into pairs?

1

2

3

4

5

6

7

8

9

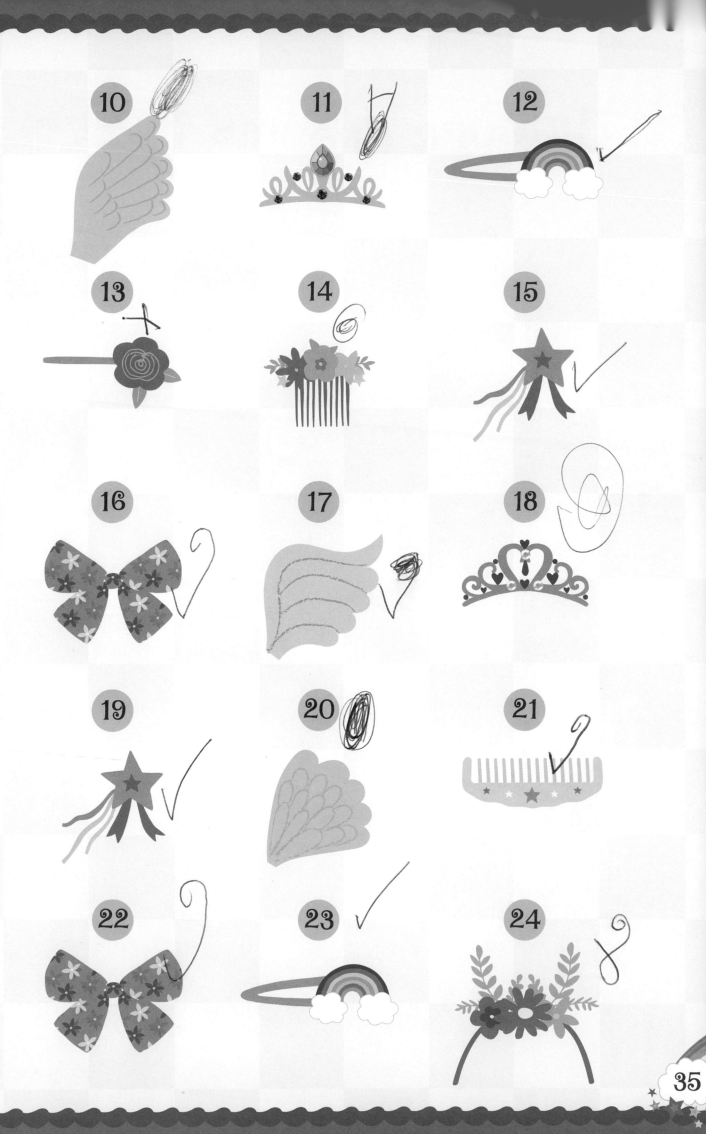

Unicorn dreams

Add some colour to finish off this picture of the unicorns galloping towards the castle.

Size up

Can you number these unicorns, from 1 to 8, with 1 for the biggest and 8 for the smallest?

Flying high

Colour by numbers and follow the colour key below to transform these unicorns.

39

Copy and colour

Can you copy these unicorns into the empty grids?

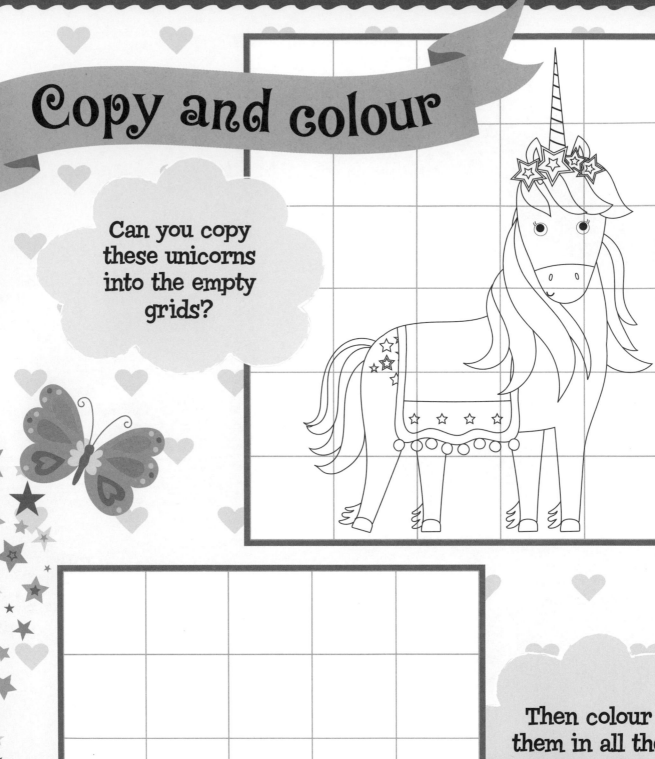

Then colour them in all the colours of the rainbow.

Bill Butterfly

Let's eat!

Meet Bill!
Did you know that
butterflies can taste
with their feet!

SPECIES: butterfly
LIVES IN: the enchanted forest
LIKES: flowers, trees
            and nectar

42

Harriet Horse

Harriet Horse is a loyal and steady friend

I wish I could fly like Sparkle Unicorn!

SPECIES: horse
LIVES IN: the enchanted forest
LIKES: sparkly gems and jewels, prancing and her unicorn friends

Ha ha! What did the mummy horse say to the baby horse? It's pasture bedtime.

43

Count up

Count up the pictures and fill in the answers below.

Fun flyers

All unicorns love to fly over the rainbow.

Some like to fly under the rainbow too.

Rainbow bright

Colour in these unicorns so they are all the colours of the rainbow.

Which way?

Start

Can you help this unicorn find her way through the meadow to discover the magical treasure?

Finish

47

Smile

Unicorns love a good selfie.
Can you doodle some of
Rainbow Unicorn's
pals below?

Rainbow Unicorn

Sparkle Unicorn

Moonbeam Unicorn

Shimmer Unicorn

Starlight Unicorn

Magical makes

What you do:

Remove this page and stick it to some card. Cut around your unicorn mask (and the small holes at the sides and the larger holes at the front).

Thread some string through the holes at the side of your mask and tie in a knot to secure the mask at the back of your head.

What you need:
- scissors
- glue
- card

49

Special treasure

What you need:
- scissors
- glue

What you do:

1. Cut along the black dotted lines to cut out the template.
2. Fold along the pink dotted lines.
3. Add glue to the flaps, where it says glue here, to attach the sides.

This will be the top (lid) of your box.

glue here   glue here

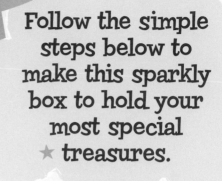

glue here   glue here

You could make your box even stronger by sticking the template to some card before folding it up and adding the glue.

Follow the steps on page 51
and use this side of the template
for your treasure box if you prefer.

This will be the
top (lid)
of your box.

glue here

glue here

glue here

glue here

Pen pot

Ask a grown-up to help you cut out your pen pot template if you find it tricky.

Use the template below to make a sparkly pot for your pens and pencils.

What you do:

1 Cut along the dotted lines to cut out the template.

2 Add some glue to the white strip.

3 Wrap the template around a cardboard roll and press the ends firmly to stick together.

What you need:
- scissors
- glue
- cardboard roll

glue here

53

Pop your pens and pencils in your pot, then use them to colour in these happy unicorns.

Follow the steps on page 53 and use this side of the template for your pen pot if you prefer.

glue here

Shhhhhhh!

Be careful not to wake the snoozing unicorns as you colour them in.

Zzz

Zzz

ZZZzzzz

ZZZzzzz

Magical moonbeams

Which path should this unicorn follow to reach the moon?

1

2

3

4

END

Seek and spot

Can you find..?

1 waterfall ✓

2 rainbows ✓

3 trees ✓

4 unicorns ✓

5 blue flowers ✓

6 unicorn shoes ✓

Moonbeam Unicorn

Moonbeam Unicorn loves to fly, dream, sleep... repeat.

SPECIES: unicorn
LIVES IN: Unicorn Castle
LIKES: daydreaming, a full moon and sleeping

Zzzzz... snore... zzzzz!

Lili Ladybird may be small but she has a big personality!

Watch me dance!

Lili Ladybird

SPECIES: ladybird
LIVES IN: the enchanted forest
LIKES: tap dancing, singing and somersaults

Ladybirds can have spots, stripes or no markings at all.

Perfect prancer

Follow this order:

Follow the spots in the order below to help the unicorn prance across the meadow to her friends. You can go up, down, left or right but not diagonally.

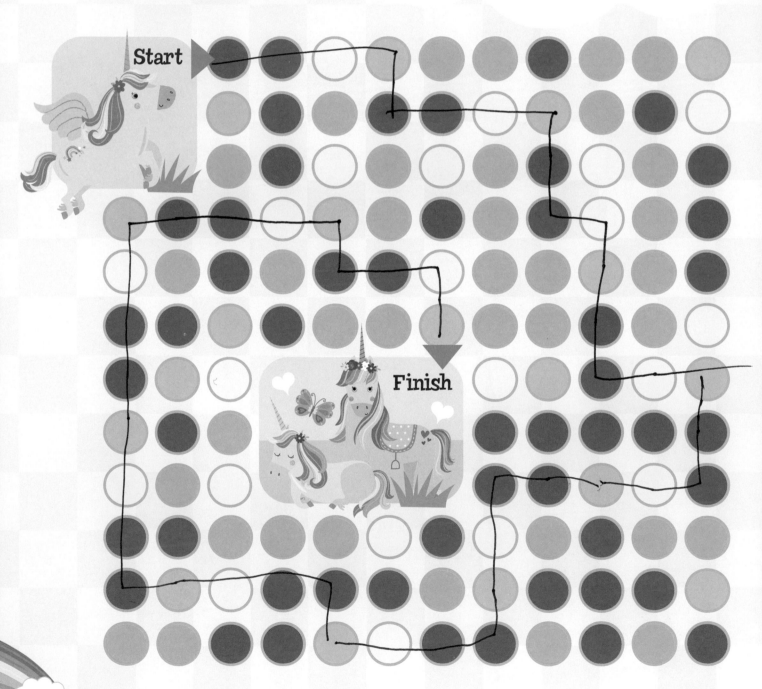

Start

Finish

60

Spot it

These small pictures may all look the same as the big picture below, but there is something different in each one. Can you spot what?

1

2

3

4

Unicorn adventure

Create your own comic-strip adventure story with some words, drawings and lots of imagination.

Oopsie!

Hair-mazing

Help this unicorn's mane look dazzling by colouring by numbers.

Spot it

Can you spot 8 differences between these pictures of flying unicorns?

65

Party time

Add some bright colours to give these unicorns the best party ever!

BFF

Colour by numbers and make these unicorns BFF.

Name game

Filbert

Fluttershy

Can you spot all of the friends in the wordsearch below? Look forwards, backwards and diagonally too.

Moonbeam

Rainbow

Shimmer

I	E	H	Y	W	G	I	U	L	Y
Z	L	A	P	O	U	L	O	I	H
M	K	R	R	B	C	A	R	N	S
O	R	R	I	N	S	H	G	B	R
O	A	I	H	I	B	I	L	L	E
N	P	E	C	A	Z	R	L	B	T
B	S	T	A	R	L	I	G	H	T
E	C	R	E	M	M	I	H	S	U
A	A	W	B	S	A	I	L	I	L
M	A	R	T	R	E	B	L	I	F

Bill

Starlight

Chirpy

Sparkle

Harriet

Lili

Seek and find

Follow the clues below to work out which friends are exploring where. When you find their location, write their initials on the map.

Find Rainbow Unicorn.
Go north 4 squares.
Head east 3 squares.
Drop south 2 squares.

Spot Chirpy Chick.
Head east 4 squares.
Go north 3 squares.
Turn west 3 squares.

Race to it and track
Moonbeam Unicorn.
Head north 6 squares.
Turn east 4 squares.
Go south 3 squares.

Where is Filbert Frog?
Move north 2 squares.
Go east 2 squares.
Head north 2 squares.

Now write some instructions to explain how to find Sparkle Unicorn.

_____

_____

_____

Find Lili Ladybird!
Head north 2 squares.
Go east 4 squares.
Move north 2 squares.

START

N
W E
S

71

Puzzle time

Draw it in the dream bubble.

cake

1

Cross out every letter that appears twice to reveal what Moonbeam Unicorn is dreaming of.

t c h a
x s h x
k t s e

2 Can you make 10 new words from the letters in the words below?

magical unicorns

ring

can

3 Can you circle every third letter to reveal Rainbow Unicorn's favourite hobby?

t m f j g l k b y
t x i j q n b v g

72

Going dotty

Join the dots to reveal where these unicorns live.

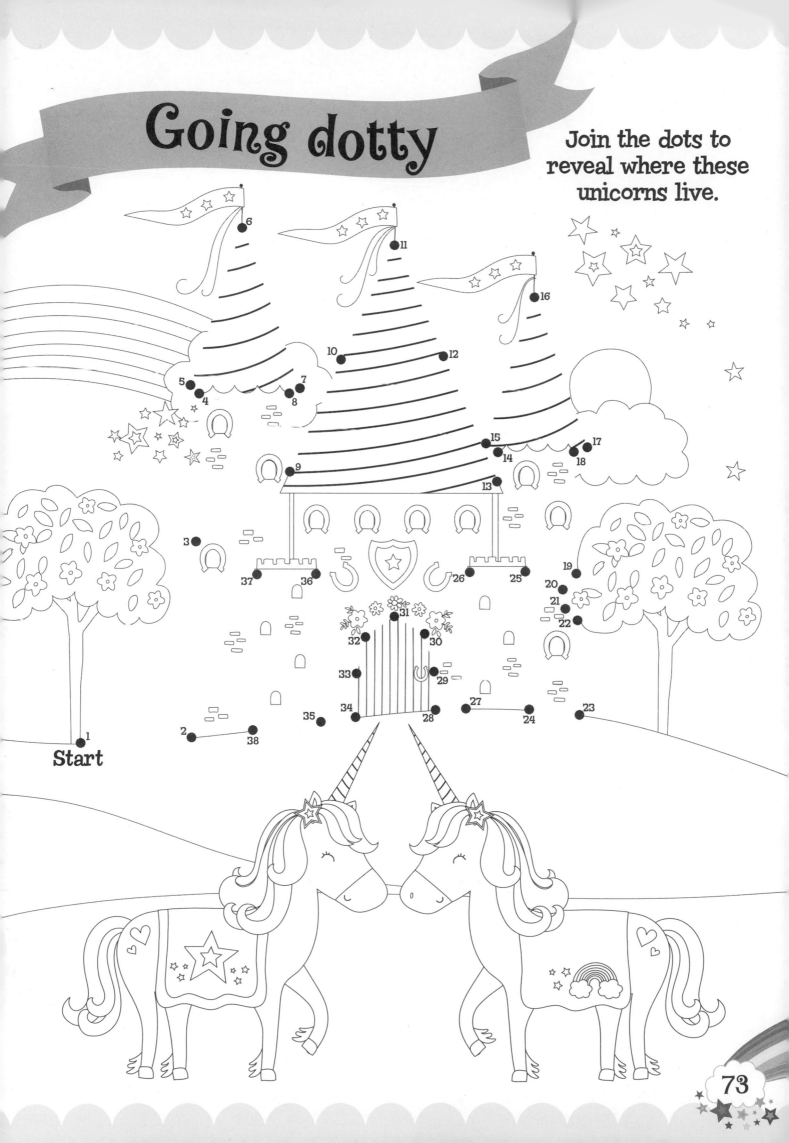

Start

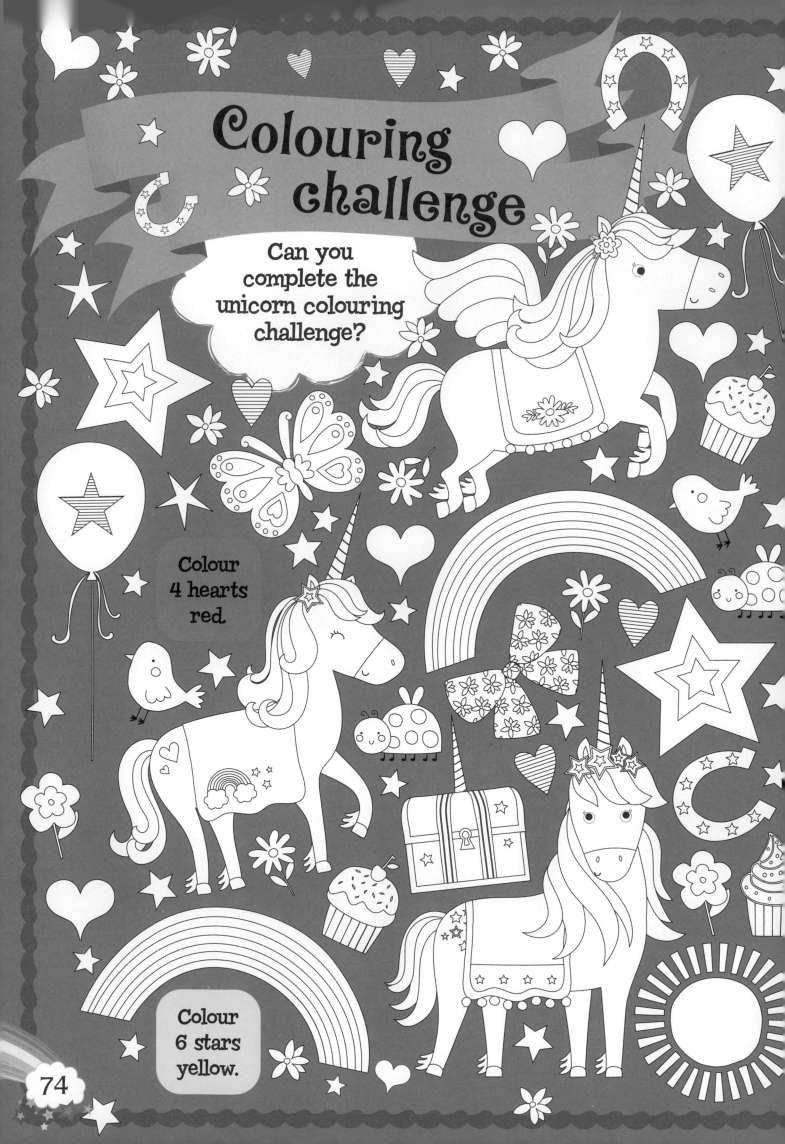

Colouring challenge

Can you complete the unicorn colouring challenge?

Colour 4 hearts red

Colour 6 stars yellow.

Colour 2 birds blue.

Colour the other pictures all the colours of the rainbow.

75

Answers

Pages 8-9

Page 22
You will find treasure at the end of the rainbow.

Page 23

Page 12

Page 13
1–B, 2–D, 3–A, 4–C

Page 18

Pages 26-27

Pages 34-35

1&14, 2&21, 3&20, 4&13, 5&24, 6&18, 7&17, 8&10, 9&11, 12&23, 15&19, 16&22

Page 38

Page 44

Page 47

Page 56
Path 2 leads to the moon

Page 57

1 waterfall
2 rainbows
3 trees
4 unicorns
5 blue flowers
6 unicorn shoes

Page 60

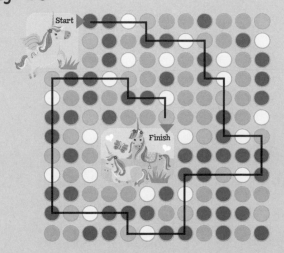

Page 61

Page 65

Page 69

I	E	H	Y	W	G	I	U	L	Y
Z	L	A	P	O	U	L	O	I	H
M	K	R	R	B	C	A	R	N	S
O	R	R	I	N	S	H	G	B	R
O	A	I	H	I	B	I	L	L	E
N	P	E	C	A	Z	R	L	B	T
B	S	T	A	R	L	I	G	H	T
E	C	R	E	M	M	I	H	S	U
A	A	W	B	S	A	I	L	I	L
M	A	R	T	R	E	B	L	I	F

Pages 70-71

Page 72

1 Cake
2 Options could include: man, girl, lag, sun, son, run, rug, arm, calm, corn, union, song, normal
3 Flying